MICKEY MOUSE CLUBHOUSE

Goofy's Missing Frog

Advance PUBLISHERS

Advance Publishers, L.C.
1060 Maitland Center Commons, Suite 365
Maitland, FL 32751 USA

10 9 8 7 6 5 4 3 2 1
ISBN-10: 1-57973-386-7

Goofy loved his pet frog, Hoppy. They had tons of fun together. They went swimming together, they surfed together, and they even rode a bicycle together.

Sometimes Hoppy was good...

FROGS

Frogs can be found all over the world. They usually live in wet areas near ponds, lakes, and rivers. Some frogs even live in trees.

...and sometimes he liked to cause trouble.

"Gawrsh!" Goofy exclaimed. "It's Hoppy!"

"Ribbit, ribbit," replied the frog.

Mickey chuckled. "I guess that's the end of our chess game!"

Goofy laughed. "A-hyuck! I think you're right."

But they do like the water.

AMPHIBIANS

Amphibians are animals that don't have hair, fur, feathers, or scales. They have wet, smooth skin. Most amphibians live in or around water because they must keep their skin a little wet.

Mickey's special telescope helps him see things that are far away.

TELESCOPES
Telescopes help us learn about planets.

The next afternoon, Goofy couldn't find Hoppy anywhere. He looked everywhere inside the Clubhouse.

"Golly, I can't think of where he hopped off to," Goofy said to his friends.

"We can help you look," Minnie suggested.
"Let's go up to the Mousekespotter and see if we can spot Hoppy," said Mickey.
But the pals didn't see Hoppy anywhere.

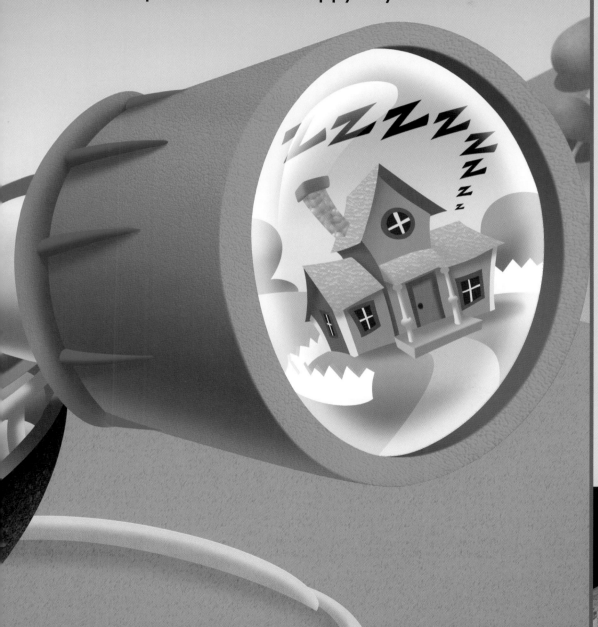

There are even telescopes floating around in space!

TELESCOPES

Scientists who study outer space are called astronomers. They use telescopes to help them see faraway objects such as planets and stars.

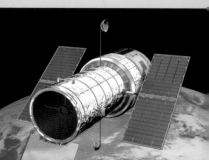

The river flows downstream.

RIVERS

Rivers and streams don't flow in a straight line. They twist and turn as they flow. Rivers start in the mountains or hills and usually end up flowing into a large body of water, such as an ocean, bay, or sea.

"Let's look outside," Daisy said. "Frogs like water. Maybe Hoppy is by the river."

When they got to the river, Mickey said, "We're going to need some Mouseketools. Everyone say, 'Oh, Toodles!'"

Toodles appeared with the Mouseketools:
a megaphone, a rowboat, a hang glider, and the
Mystery Mouseketool.

"Which Mouseketool will help us get down the river?" asked Mickey.

"This one," said Minnie, pointing to the rowboat.

Goofy is getting lots of fresh water!

STREAMS

A stream is a small, flowing body of water. The water in rivers and streams is not salty like the water in an ocean. They have what is called freshwater.

It's a good thing Goofy wasn't trying to go down the longest river in the world!

NILE RIVER

The Nile River is the longest river in the world. It is 4,184 miles long! Located in Africa, the Nile flows through nine countries and empties into the Mediterranean Sea.

"You betcha!" said Mickey. "We've got ears! Say cheers!"

Goofy offered to go in the rowboat. He wasn't very far before the boat sprung a leak.

"Gawrsh, I need more boots just to empty out the water!" he said.

TURTLES

As soon as this turtle hatched, it headed straight to the water for its very first swim! This turtle is growing up. Now it mostly eats bugs. When it gets bigger, it will munch on plants, too.

"I have an idea," said Donald. "I'm going to look under the water."

He put on a scuba mask and dived in. He didn't spot anything under the water, but he saw a frog on top.

"I found him!" Donald said. He pointed to a frog sitting on a lily pad.

"Aw," said Mickey. "That's not Hoppy."

Donald grumbled. "Aw, phooey!"

"Let's keep looking," Mickey said, as he helped his pal out of the water.

"I don't remember seeing that duck here before," said the turtle.

TURTLES

Many turtles live in the water. Different kinds of turtles can be found in streams, ponds, and in the sea. Other kinds of turtles live on land. You can even find turtles out in the desert!

Nature is full of sounds.

SOUNDS

Sounds fill the air during the day. Dogs bark and bees buzz. You can also hear birds whistle and sing. They call to one another through the trees.

"No sign of Hoppy yet?" Goofy asked when he saw his friends.

"Nope," replied Mickey. "Have you tried calling to him?"

"I did," said Goofy. "But maybe he didn't hear me."

"Maybe Toodles can help," said Mickey. "Oh, Toodles!" said Mickey.

Toodles brought a megaphone for Goofy. That would make his voice sound really loud. Goofy called into the megaphone. "Is this loud enough?"

"I'll say!" Mickey said, covering his ears.

Many animals don't need a megaphone!

NOISES

Dogs can hear very high and very low noises that humans cannot. In fact, they can detect sounds that are four times farther away than humans are able to hear!

It looks like Pluto's ears are almost as long as this rabbit's!

RABBITS

A rabbit's long ears can turn in any direction to help it hear even the faintest sounds. Rabbits will thump their hind legs to let other rabbits know when they sense danger.

Goofy used the megaphone to call to Hoppy, but the only creatures that came were rabbits. Lots and lots of rabbits!

Everyone was surprised. Pluto was so surprised, he forgot to bark!

"They sure are cute," Mickey said.

"Aw, but they aren't Hoppy," said Goofy. "Don't worry, pal," Mickey said. "We'll find him. I promise."

These rabbits probably came from the same burrow.

RABBITS

Rabbits usually live in groups in underground burrows. They eat grass, bark, leaves, and berries.

Just like Goofy's hang glider, these sails use the wind to go.

WIND

Although you can't see the wind, you can feel it moving through the air. Wind can be very strong and powerful, making leaves and kites zip through the air, or it can feel like a soft, gentle whisper against your skin.

"What if we look for him from up there?" said Minnie, pointing to the sky.

"Gee, that's a great idea," said Goofy. "But how will we get up there?"

"I'll bet one of our Mouseketools can help us," said Mickey. "Oh, Toodles!"

Toodles flew in with the last two Mouseketools: a hang glider and the Mystery Mouseketool.

Goofy picked the hang glider. "I'll take it and meet you back at the Clubhouse."

"Great!" said Mickey. "And we'll keep looking down here."

Goofy took a running leap and flew into the air, holding on tight to the hang glider. He flew through the air. He didn't see Hoppy, but he did see an angry bear!

Bears are very hungry when they wake up from their long winter nap.

BEARS
Eating! When grizzly bears wake from their long winter naps, they are hungry. They come to the tundra in the spring.

PIGS

Pigs live on farms. And there is nothing they like more than a roll in the mud. The mud cools them off on a hot day.

Meanwhile, the rest of the friends piled into the Toon Car to search near the roads. Suddenly, Mickey pressed on the brakes.

A large pig was blocking the road. How could they get it to move?

"I think it's time for the Mystery Mouseketool," said Mickey.

The Mystery Mouseketool was corn! Donald used the corn to tempt the pig away from the road.

"Super cheers! We've used all our Mouseketools!" said Mickey.

To get to the corn!

CORN

In some places, corn is harvested in the fall. The farmer uses a special truck called a combine to pick the corn. The combine takes the husks and the kernels off the cob. The farmer can then use the corn to feed cows or other farm animals.

When Goofy and his friends met up again by the pond, there was still no sign of Hoppy. Then they heard a familiar ribbit.

Minnie giggled. "Goofy, I think your hat is ribbiting!"

"Oh, boy! I was wondering where my hat went," said Goofy. "It fell off while I was hang gliding."

"Well, it looks like Hoppy found it," said Daisy.

"And he found us, too," added Mickey. "Hot dog!"

Goofy happily picked up his hat—and his frog!

CATTAILS
Cattails are grasses that grow in ponds.

LAKES

Lakes and ponds
are home to many
plants and animals.
Bright green lily
pads with pretty
flowers grow in
ponds. They are
a nice place for
frogs to take a rest.

Some frogs are really large. Imagine if Hoppy were this big!

GOLIATH FROG

The Goliath frog is the largest kind of frog in the world. It lives in rivers in Africa and can grow to be the size of a large house cat. This hoppity fellow can jump 10 feet in a single bound.

Before long, Hoppy took a giant leap and hopped away again. Mickey chased after him.
Goofy followed. "A-hyuck! Here we go again!"